The Old Days

 **SRA**

Columbus, OH

SRAonline.com

 SRA

Send all inquiries to this address:
SRA/McGraw-Hill
4400 Easton Commons
Columbus, OH 43219

ISBN: 978-0-07-608568-2
MHID: 0-07-608568-6

2 3 4 5 6 7 8 9 NOR 13 12 11 10 09

The McGraw-Hill Companies

Mac and his grandfather were in the attic. Mac found a hat made from leather. He slipped it onto his head.

"My father wore that hat on the apple farm," said Poppy.

"Do I look like him?" asked Mac.

"A little," said Poppy.

Poppy showed Mac a photo.

"This is my father," said Poppy. "His parents started the farm after they moved to the United States."

"Were you a farmer too?" asked Mac.

"I worked on the farm when I was your age," said Poppy.

"Did you have lots of chores to do?" asked
Mac. "I have so many chores at home." He made
a funny face.

Poppy smiled and nodded. "Farming was hard work," he said. "Everyone helped pick the apples. We grew other crops too."

Mac saw a big blue ribbon and pinned it to his shirt. "Who won this?" he asked.

"The mayor awarded my mother that ribbon for her apple pie!" said Poppy. "Her pies were popular. We sold them at the farm stand."

"Life was fun in the old days!" said Mac.
"Yes, it was," said Poppy. "And this is fun too!"

Vocabulary

leather (leth´ ər) (page 3) *n.* Material made from animal skin.

slipped (slipt) (page 3) *v.* Past tense of **slip:** To put on.

chores (chôrz) (page 7) *n.* Plural form of **chore:** A small job around the house.

crops (krops) (page 8) *n.* Plural form of **crop:** Fruits, vegetables, or other plants that are grown on a farm and sold.

awarded (ə wôr´ dəd) (page 10) *v.* Past tense of **award:** To give a prize.

popular (pop´ yə lər) (page 10) *adj.* Liked or accepted by many people.

Comprehension Focus: Fact and Opinion

1. Name one fact that Poppy tells Mac about farm life.

2. Name one of Poppy's opinions about life in the old days.